Albert
and the Wind

Ian Brown and Eoin Clarke

GRAFFEG

Albert set off to
find his flying food.

5

"Hello," said a bee with a leaf. "This just blew into my face. I think it belongs to you."

"To make sure it does not blow away again, I am going to sit on it," said Albert.

"That should work," said the bee.

Albert walked forward and gently lowered his shell onto the leaf.

He looked up, saying, "Oh..."

But, before he could say what he wanted to say, the bee had buzzed off.

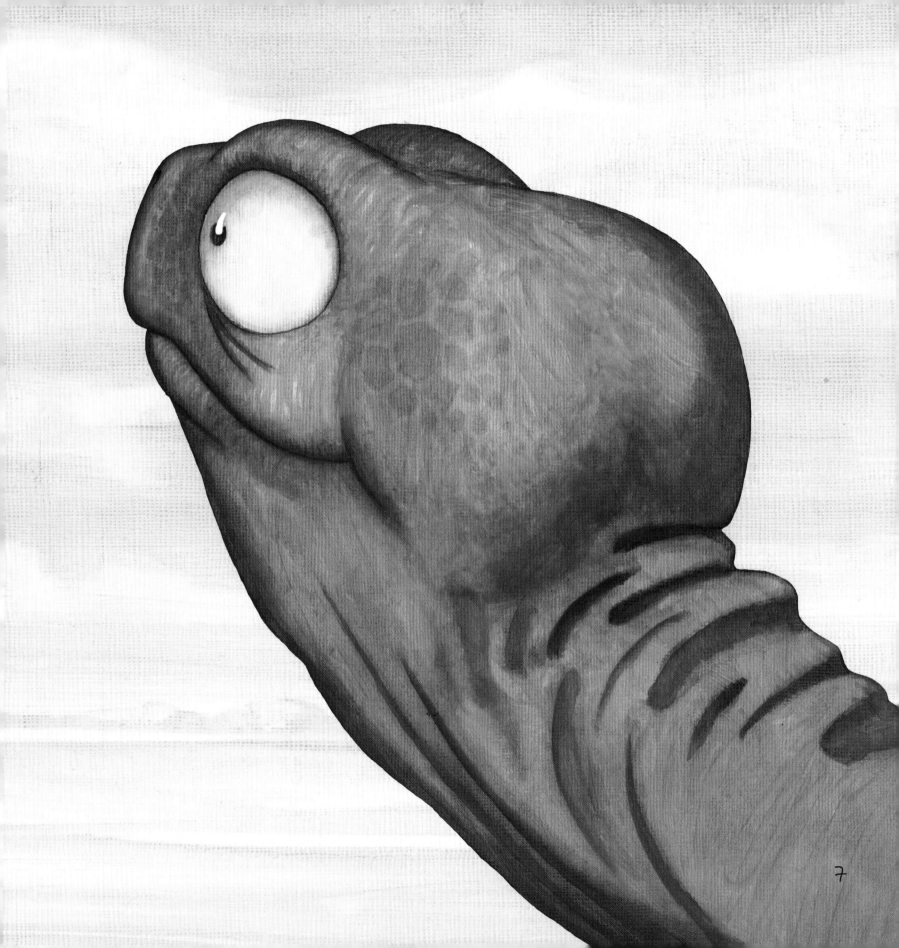

7

"Hello," said a spider. "I was sitting in my web when your flowers got caught in it. With my sticky thread on them, they should not blow away again."

"To be sure, I am going to sit on them," said Albert.

And he did. Slowly.

Albert looked up, saying, "Oh, th..."

But, before he could say what he wanted to say, the spider had crept away.

"Greetings," said a snail. "I was slithering around the plant pots when all this tomato rolled past. With my gloop, it should not blow away again."

Albert went to speak, but, before he could say what he wanted to say, the snail had slipped away.

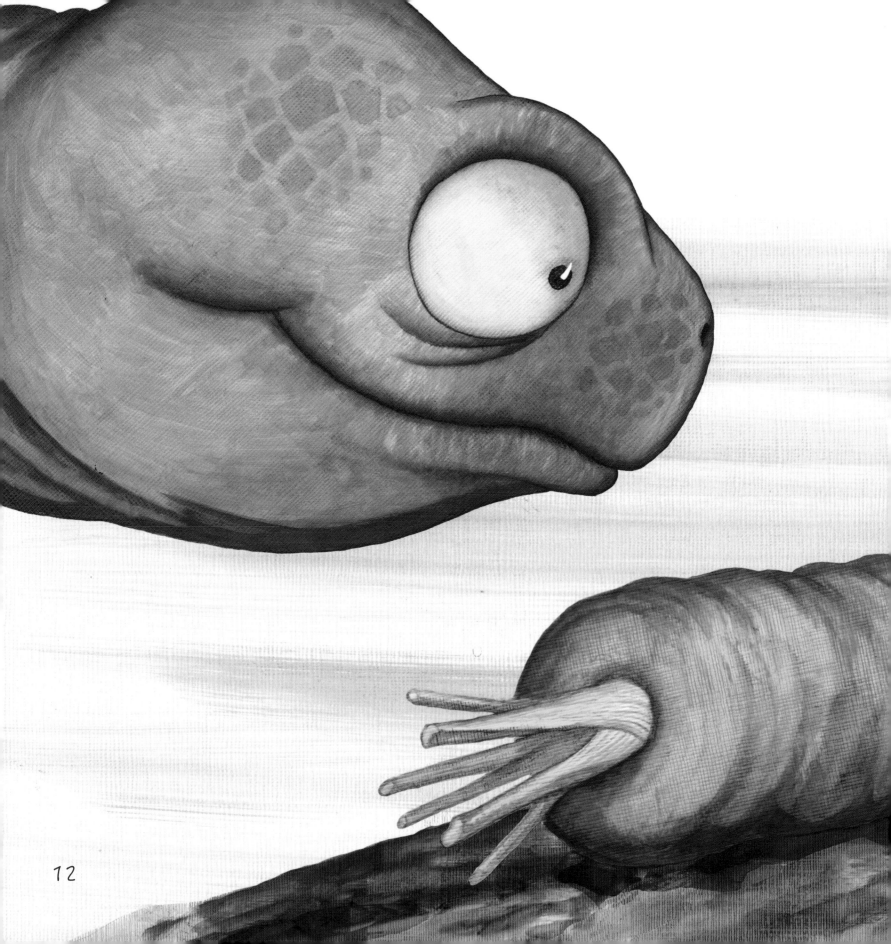

"Hello," said a worm. "This carrot bounced over my head. It has some sticky mud on it now, so might not blow away again."

"To make sure, I will sit on it," said Albert.

He started to say, "Oh, tha..."

But, before he could finish, the worm had wriggled away.

Word spread all over about Albert's lost food. Creatures emerged from every corner of the garden to join in.

14

Some did not fully
understand and delivered
items that had nothing to
do with the meal.

16

Still the wind blew.

A fly and a bee went bumbling by.

Other things were blown off course too.

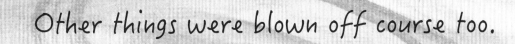

But, steadily, Albert was reunited with more of his food.

"Excuse us," whispered a pair of shy woodlice. "This celery blew under the plant pot where we hide. We do not need it."

"To keep it safe, I shall sit on it," said Albert.

He looked across, saying, "Oh, than..."

But, before he could say what he wanted to say, the woodlice had scurried away.

"Hello," said a troop of ants in unison. "We were tidying our area and this cucumber rolled in. We like to be tidy."

"I will sit on it so it does not cause a mess," said Albert.

He started to say, "Oh, thank..."

But, before he could say any more, the ants had marched off, very tidily.

"At last, I have all my meal back," thought Albert. "Everyone was so kind. But I never had the chance to say what I meant to say."

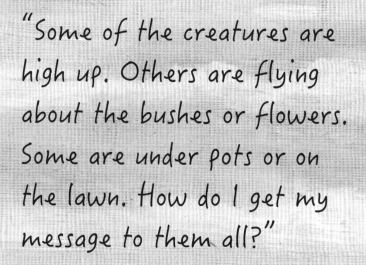

"Some of the creatures are high up. Others are flying about the bushes or flowers. Some are under pots or on the lawn. How do I get my message to them all?"

His tummy gurgled again... and he had an idea.

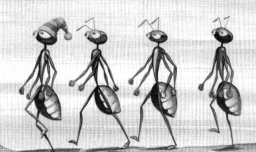

26

He reversed off his pile of food
and, bit by bit, munched away.

But he did not eat all of it.

When he had finished, he spun
around to point his bottom at
the remains of the food.
His tummy gurgled in a
different way.

27

He was hungry and ready to eat the food that had been left for him.

He opened his mouth wide and swung his head at the food with a big, snapping bite... But there was nothing there. The wind had blown it all away!

Swoosh! Whoo! Wharr! The noise of the wind woke
Albert the tortoise. His tummy gurgled.

Suddenly, a loud noise burst from Albert's back end. PaaaAAAARRRRRPPP!

It blasted pieces of tomato, celery, cucumber and carrot into the air.

The wind caught them and they flew all around the garden, spelling out Albert's special message for everyone that had helped him. THANK YOU.

His food was not the only thing
blasted into the air.

Albert looked round,
saying, "Pardon me."

Ian Brown

Ian is a former journalist turned television writer and producer. After a spell on local and national newspapers, a thirty-year career in television has included news, documentaries, commercials, comedy and entertainment shows. He has written or produced for a host of household names, picking up several awards along the way. He's also often heard on radio talking about television. Writing for children has been a long-held dream. Ian shares his home with, among others, wife Millie, two cats and a tortoise called Albert.

Eoin Clarke

Eoin qualified with a BA in Graphic Design from Middlesex University and an MA in Animation from the Royal College of Art. He has worked for thirty years in the animation industry as a director, animator, designer and storyboard artist. Eoin has directed films, commercials, documentaries and title sequences and picked up thirty awards as a director, working on projects for, among others, the BBC, Channel 4 and the British Film Institute. Helping bring Albert to life has been a joy.

Albert

Albert, who inspired these adventures, was rescued more than fifty years ago by Ian's wife and her family. He has lived happily with the same family ever since. You can get to know the real Albert better on facebook, @AlbertTheTortoise, and on twitter, @AlbertTortoise.

Facts about Albert and his cousins

Albert in this story is based on a real tortoise – also called Albert – a modern-day mini-dinosaur living life on the veg...

1. Real Albert might be 80 years old. He is a Greek tortoise – also known as Mediterranean spur-thighed. Despite the name, they're also found in Northern Africa, Southern Europe and parts of the Middle East. They have little fleshy spurs on their thighs, near the tail.

2. The food shown in this book is for the story. Greek tortoises like Albert eat vegetation. They were vegan long before its current popularity. In real life, different types of tortoises eat different types of food. For real Albert, good foods include grasses that can be grazed from a lawn, dandelions, clover, leafy salads, watercress, spring greens, coriander and parsley. The bulk of the food should be leafy greens and grasses. Small amounts of strawberry or grated carrot can be monthly treats. There are a few species of tortoise that can safely eat more fruit, but most can't.

3. Real Albert's food has actually blown away from him on windy days.

4. Tortoises are intelligent. Studies have shown them to have long memories and indicate they can be trained.

5. Tortoise shells are complicated structures and contain 60 interconnected bones.

6. The scales on a tortoise shell are known as scutes. On the outer shell, they are made of the same material – known as keratin – that makes up human fingernails. This protects against injury, infection and damage.

7. A group of tortoises is called a 'creep', and two or more tortoises will sometimes share a burrow. Nevertheless, most tortoises are seen as loners who prefer their own company.

8. Tortoises can hold their breath for a surprising amount of time. They empty their lungs before going back into their shell and can last for quite a while before coming out for oxygen. If they sense a threat, you can often hear them breathe out before going into their shell.

9. It's not easy to tell if a tortoise is a boy or girl. This can only happen when they reach maturity. The plastron (the bottom part of the shell) is usually the best way to tell. It is normally flatter for females and more curved for males. Also, males usually have larger tails than the females.

10. Tortoises smell with their throats. As is common with other reptiles, tortoises use the roof of their mouth to smell. This is where the vomeronasal organ (also known as Jacobson's organ) is located.

11. Always seek specialist advice before considering a tortoise as a pet and always consult expert guidance on tortoise care.

Albert and the Wind
Published in Great Britain in 2021 by Graffeg Limited.

ISBN 9781913733445

Written by Ian Brown copyright © 2021.
Illustrated by Eoin Clarke copyright © 2021.
Designed and produced by Graffeg Limited
copyright © 2021.

Graffeg Limited, 15 Neptune Court, Vanguard Way, Cardiff,
CF24 5PJ, Wales, UK. Tel: +44(0)1554 824000.
www.graffeg.com.

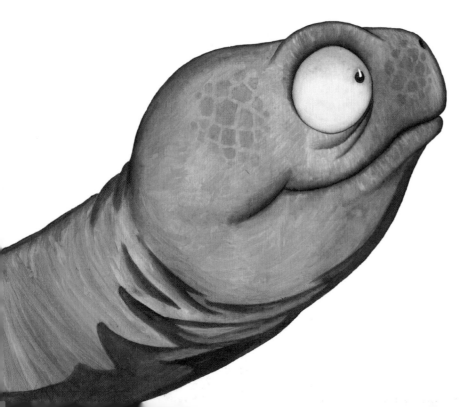